最佳午餐竞选

[美]伊莲娜·梅◎著
[美]黛安·帕尔米夏诺◎绘
范晓星◎译

天津出版传媒集团
新蕾出版社

送给所有的孩子们。

——伊莲娜·梅

图书在版编目 (CIP) 数据

最佳午餐竞选 / (美) 伊莲娜·梅 (Eleanor May) 著 ; (美) 黛安·帕尔米夏诺 (Diane Palmisciano) 绘 ; 范晓星译.-- 天津:新蕾出版社,2016.8(2024.12 重印)
(数学帮帮忙·互动版)
书名原文: Mac & Cheese, Pleeeeze!
ISBN 978-7-5307-6438-1

Ⅰ.①最… Ⅱ. ①伊…②黛…③范… Ⅲ. ①数学-儿童读物Ⅳ. ①O1-49

中国版本图书馆 CIP 数据核字(2016)第 157764 号

出版发行: 天津出版传媒集团
新蕾出版社
http://www.newbuds.com.cn
地　　址: 天津市和平区西康路 35 号(300051)
出 版 人: 马玉秀
电　　话: 总编办(022)23332422
发行部(022)23332679　23332351
传　　真: (022)23332422
经　　销: 全国新华书店
印　　刷: 天津新华印务有限公司
开　　本: 787mm×1092mm　1/16
印　　张: 3
版　　次: 2016 年 8 月第 1 版　2024 年 12 月第 20 次印刷
定　　价: 12.00 元

无处不在的数学

资深编辑　卢　江

人们常说“兴趣是最好的老师”，有了兴趣，学习就会变得轻松愉快。数学对于孩子来说或许有些难，因为比起语文，数学显得枯燥、抽象，不容易理解，孩子往往不那么喜欢。可许多家长都知道，学数学对于孩子的成长和今后的生活有多么重要。不仅数学知识很有用，学习数学过程中获得的数学思想和方法更会影响孩子的一生，因为数学素养是构成人基本素质的一个重要因素。但是，怎样才能让孩子对数学产生兴趣呢？怎样才能激发他们兴致勃勃地去探索数学问题呢？我认为，让孩子读些有趣的书或许是不错的选择。读了这套“数学帮帮忙”，我立刻产生了想把它们推荐给教师和家长朋友们的愿望，因为这真是一套会让孩子爱上数学的好书！

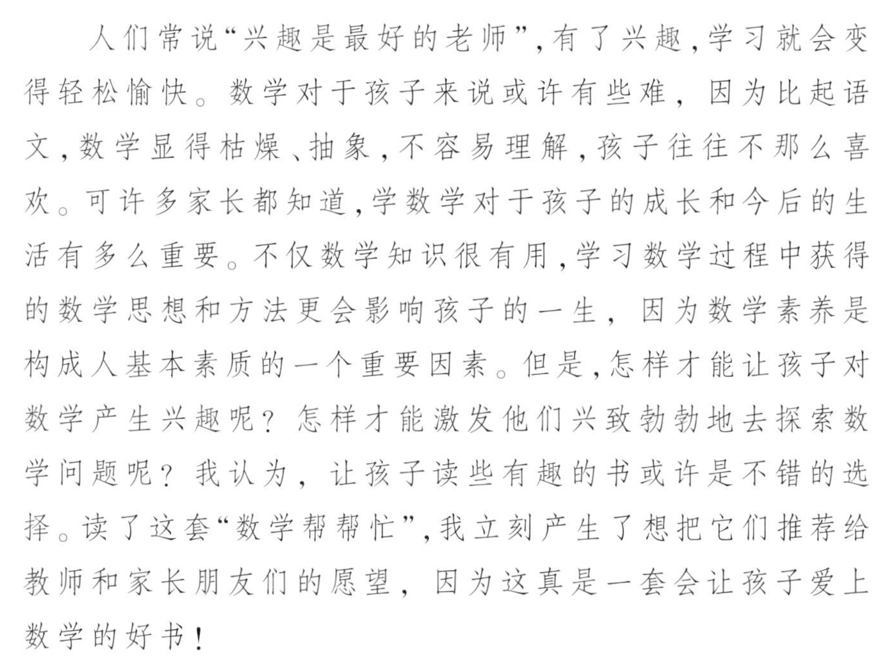

这套有趣的图书从美国引进，原出版者是美国资深教育专家。每本书讲述一个孩子们生活中的故事，由故事中出现的问题自然地引入一个数学知识，然后通过运用数学知识解决问题。比如，从帮助外婆整理散落的纽扣引出分类，从为小狗记录藏骨头的地点引出空间方位等等。故事素材全部来源于孩子们的真实生活，不是童话，不是幻想，而是鲜活的生活实例。正是这些发生在孩子身边的故事，让孩子们懂得，数学无处不在并且非常有用；这些鲜活的实例也使得抽象的概念更易于理解，更容易激发孩子学习数学的兴趣，让他们逐渐爱上数学。这样的教育思想和方法与我国近年来提倡的数学教育理念是十分吻合的！

这是一套适合5~8岁孩子阅读的书，书中的有趣情节和生动的插画可以将抽象的数学问题直观化、形象化，为孩子的思维活动提供具体形象的支持。如果亲子共读的话，家长可以带领孩子推测情节的发展，探讨解决难题的办法，让孩子在愉悦的氛围中学到知识和方法。

值得教师和家长朋友们注意的是，在每本书的后面，出版者还加入了“互动课堂”及“互动练习”，一方面通过一些精心设计的活动让孩子巩固新学到的数学知识，进一步体会知识的含义和实际应用；另一方面帮助家长指导孩子阅读，体会故事中数学之外的道理，逐步提升孩子的阅读理解能力。

我相信孩子读过这套书后一定会明白，原来，数学不是烦恼，不是包袱，数学真能帮大忙！

我喜欢我的老师——莫尔老师。我真的特别喜欢他。不过，他总是有好多稀奇古怪的想法。

“最佳午餐竞选？”我百思不得其解，“选肉饼市长、比萨总统吗？”

我的好朋友露娜笑着说：“哦，得了吧，凯琳。我觉得挺有意思的。”

“同学们，”上午，莫尔老师在课上对大家说，“我们要举行最佳午餐竞选。”

“啊？”我们都不明白。

莫尔老师解释道：“每个同学给自己最喜欢的午餐投票，最受欢迎的午餐将会作为学校春季宴会的主菜。你们要努力为自己最喜欢的午餐拉票。全校同学都参加哟！祝大家好运，让最棒的午餐当选！”

“肯定一团糟。”放学后我对露娜说，“还记得上个月的科学作业吗？”

没错，我们都喜欢蚯蚓农场，但上次山姆和乔伊吵得不可开交，把蚯蚓农场弄翻了，地板上全是泥土和扭来扭去的蚯蚓，大家的兴致一下都没了。

“那个太恶心了。”露娜也表示同意，“不过这次是午餐啊，没有泥土，也没有蚯蚓。至少，我希望没有！”

露娜和我停下来看莫尔老师的竞选规则。

“什么意思？”我嘟囔道，“每个人都会选比萨饼的。”

“我就不选。”露娜说，“我要选我最喜欢的——健康豆腐。”

有时候，露娜可真是跟莫尔老师一样古怪。

我把竞选这事忘了，直到第二天坐上校车时，我才想起来。

“看我的竞选海报！我选的是金枪鱼三明治。”安妮说。

我瞪大了眼睛问：“你还做了竞选海报？”

安妮打开一张海报，让我看她的竞选口号。

山姆不服气地说:“你没戏的。等着听我的西兰花烤土豆获胜吧!”

我摇摇头说:“真是难以置信,你们俩竟然对这种莫名其妙的竞选这么上心。”

“难道你不关心吗?”安妮问。

“呵呵,是呀。”我说,“西兰花大战金枪鱼,真是一部大片!”

我在学校看了一下报名的名单。唉，我觉得我必须选一种了。

等一下，还没有人选奶酪通心粉吗？不会吧！那是午餐菜单上最好吃的了！我把我的名字写在了奶酪通心粉的旁边。

“不错哟！”安妮说，“不过，它没有金枪鱼三明治好吃。”

午餐时，我津津有味地吃着奶酪通心粉，而露娜在数选票。“我弟弟和他国际象棋俱乐部的朋友都跟我保证投健康豆腐的票。”她告诉我。

“真的？他们喜欢吃这道菜？”

露娜脸红了。“我弟弟说要是他们选健康豆腐，他就请他们吃甜甜圈。”

正在埋头看笔记本的乔伊抬起头来。

“你在数比萨饼得了多少票吗？”我问。

“不是。我是在数所有午餐的得票数。你看到了吗？目前，第一名是美味比萨饼。第二名是……”

我停下来问：“西兰花烤土豆？”

“山姆一定没少游说。”乔伊说。

“奶酪通心粉排第几呢？”我问乔伊。

他拿笔记本给我看：“垫底呢。”

我真不敢相信。奶酪通心粉竟然还不如火鸡香肠！

太丢人了。我得去拉票！

我找到我妹妹苏菲,她正在荡秋千。“你打算投票给哪个午餐?”我问她。

“美味比萨饼呀。”

“可我需要投给奶酪通心粉的票。”

苏菲笑了:“好吧。”

“这么说,你会投票给奶酪通心粉了?”

“不,我还是喜欢美味比萨饼。”

苏菲的朋友瑞秋说:“要是你推我荡秋千,我就选奶酪通心粉。”

现在,我稳得了2票——瑞秋1票,我1票。如果我这样拉票的话,我的胳膊都要掉了!

我看到邻居查理在滑梯上。“你会投奶酪通心粉的票吗？”我问。

“山姆想让我投西兰花烤土豆的票呢。”

我刚要走开，却听到他说：“可你是我的邻居,而且西兰花很难吃。”

现在有3票了。哈哈,多好的开始！如果我不想输得很惨的话,还要多拉几票。

我还能找谁拉票呢？我不能问我的同班同学。他们都会投给自己的午餐。

我可以去问问查理的弟弟——尼克。他也是我邻居，虽然他只是个学前班的小不点儿。

“尼克，你喜欢吃奶酪通心粉吗？”

“我刚吃过啊，我不饿。”

“那你饿的时候喜欢吗？”

“我还不饿呢。”

后来，我说服了所有的小不点儿选了奶酪通心粉，除了尼克。他还是说他不饿。

又多了4票！

上数学课的时候，我一直在琢磨我的竞选口号。露娜探过身说：“我还以为你不参加竞选呢。”

“就是不想啊。”我说着，合上了笔记本。唉，我这张臭嘴，真希望我没有笑话过那些拉票的同学呀。

第二天，几个五年级的女生看到我在贴竞选海报。“好可爱呀！”一个人说，“我这票投给你啦。我爱吃奶酪通心粉！”

她的朋友们也都说：“我也爱吃。”

太好啦！又多了3票。我有10票了。我开始喜欢上这个竞选活动了！

我也想像露娜一样，在本子上把所有得票加起来。可要是被人看到，他们就知道我特别想要拉票了，这可太丢人了！

山姆也在贴竞选海报。

我看了以后，不禁笑出了声。

然后，我又看到另一张竞选海报。

哼，一点儿都不可笑。

足球队的两个同学在看我的海报。我偷偷凑过去，听一个人说："我更喜欢美味比萨饼。"

另一个女生说："是呀，可是飞碟队投比萨饼。我们不能跟他们一样。"

"绝对不可以！"男生同意，"那咱们足球队的票都给奶酪通心粉吧。"

哈哈！那可是20票呢！

某些特殊形式的数字相加时，我们可以用特别的方法计算，比如我们可以根据1+2=3，推算出10+20=30。

教室里，露娜一副垂头丧气的样子。“他们不做健康豆腐了。厨师说因为喜欢的人太少了。你相信吗？”

我耸了耸肩膀，但其实我相信。

“现在，国际象棋俱乐部不能把票投给健康豆腐了。”露娜意味深长地看了我一眼，“真是的，你又不在乎输赢，要不然我们就把这些票都投给奶酪通心粉了。”

我四下打量一下，确定没有人会听到。“我也在乎嘛，只是有那么一点点在乎哟！”我小声承认。

露娜笑了：“哦，这样的话……”

国际象棋俱乐部有 28 个同学，加上露娜是 29 人。我又多了 29 票！

想一想

30 加 20 是 50，再加上 9，就是 59 了。

在合唱班练习的时候，我对旁边的女孩小声说："合唱班的同学要齐心协力哟！投奶酪通心粉一票。告诉下一个。"

这句话一个传一个。大家都点头微笑。成了！又多了 13 票。

回家的路上，我碰到查理。

“你猜怎么着？”查理说，“我说服全班同学明天投票给奶酪通心粉了，除了蒂米。他的姐姐安妮说他会把票投给金枪鱼三明治。”

我又得了 31 票！太棒啦！

想一想

我知道 72+30=102，再加 1 就是 103 了。

课间的时候，乔伊走过来说："你不是垫底的了！"

"哦？"我假装没那么有兴趣，"这么说我超过火鸡香肠了？"

"不止这样！"他说，"现在美味比萨饼和西兰花烤土豆并列第一，接下来就是奶酪通心粉了！"

太棒啦！我跟乔伊和山姆只差一票！

下课后,安妮冲到我面前。

“你听说了吗?”她说,“山姆和乔伊打起来了,因为山姆在美味比萨饼的广告上说‘吃比萨饼变大饼脸!’现在莫尔老师不让他们投票了!”

美味比萨饼少了一票,西兰花烤土豆也少了一票。太棒啦!我们的三个菜并列第一了!

现在,我只要再多拉一票……

“苏菲，你是我妹妹。”我说，“你就不能投奶酪通心粉一票吗？”

她把小铲子立在沙堆里说：“美味比萨饼。”

哼，还是我的亲妹妹呢。这时，尼克看着我说：“我饿了，我要奶酪通心粉。”

这就是说……

“太棒啦！”我欢呼，“奶酪通心粉，你最爱的午餐！”

我高兴得又蹦又跳。露娜过来跟我击掌庆祝。

安妮惊讶地盯着我说：“我以为你会说这个竞选多好笑呢。”

“是特好笑。”我说，“还特古怪。可我特盼着能赢！”

春季宴会
投票结果
第一名 奶酪通心粉——104票
并列第二名 西兰花烤土豆——103票
美味比萨饼——103票
奶酪＋通心粉＝好吃！

整数拆分

运用整数拆分的方法，让计算变得简单吧！

根据例题所示，试着回答下面的问题。

例题：6+8=？

想一想：6+4=10

8 由 2 个 4 组成。

所以 6+8=14。

1. 48+15=？

提示：把整数拆分开会更简单。

48 + 2 + 10 + 3

50 + 10 + 3

60 + 3

？

15 是由 2、10 和 3 组成的。

答案：48+15=48+2+10+3
=50+10+3=63

2. 24+81=？

提示：两位数相加可以分解成十位数与十位数相加，个位数与个位数相加。

24	=	20	+	4
+ 81	=	80	+	1
		100	+	5 = ?

我可以把个位数先加起来，再将十位数也加起来，最后将两个结果相加。

答案：24+81=20+4+80+1
=20+80+4+1
=100+5
=105

亲爱的家长朋友，请您和孩子一起完成下面这些内容，会有更大的收获哟！

提高阅读能力

- 请您同孩子一起阅读封面上的书名、作者等信息。让孩子猜一猜封面上的小主人公在做什么？这个故事可能会讲什么？
- 大声朗读这个故事。让孩子验证下自己的猜想是否准确。
- 请看第 8 页，故事一开始凯琳对最佳午餐竞选有什么想法？后来她又是怎么改变了想法？
- 凯琳是如何不让同班同学发现其实她很在乎竞选的？她为什么不想让别人知道这个秘密呢？
- 凯琳是怎样为自己选的菜拉票的呢？

巩固数学概念

- 乔伊是如何计票的？凯琳又是如何计票的？
- 翻到第 28 页，安妮跟凯琳说了什么消息？这个消息对投票有影响吗？
- 请看第 29 页，尼克告诉凯琳他饿了，这个会对投票结果产生什么影响？
- 假设莫尔老师允许乔伊和山姆投票，最后的投票结果会有什么变化？

生活中的数学

- 请用第 24 页“想一想”的计算方法，算出 40+19=？
- 请用第 25 页“想一想”的计算方法，算出 66+27=？
- 假设你有 76 张游戏卡，你的朋友有 23 张，那么你们二人加起来有多少张呢？（提示：用第 26 页“想一想”的方法来计算。）
- 尝试用“心算”的方法算出 100+100+53=？

互动练习！

凯琳、山姆和乔伊在参与最佳午餐竞选，请你帮他们列出算式，并分别计算出目前的得票数吧！

我原来有 3 票，刚又拉来了 5 票，现在有多少票呢？

我原来有 5 票，现在又多了 4 票，我现在是不是票数最多？

昨天给美味比萨饼投票的有 4 人，今天有 2 人，我今天排在第几？

依此类推，你能将 8、9 也进行拆分吗？如果换成 70、80、90，你能进行整 10 数的拆分吗？

互动练习3

凯琳和露娜一起去文具店买东西，她们一共买了3件商品，商品的价格分别为：钢笔7元、文具盒18元、笔记本5元。请你帮她们计算下一共要花多少钱？

互动练习4

电视台要播放一部 30 集的电视连续剧，若要求每天安排播出的集数互不相等，则该电视连续剧最多可以播几天？

互动练习5

凯琳买了12个苹果，她打算将其分成3组，且每组的数量各不相同，一共可以有几种分法呢？

互动练习6
快来算一算黑板上的这些算数题吧！
32+76=
58+49=
20+30+51=
80+20+35=

互动练习7

请你尝试运用整数拆分的方法，在下列算式中填入合适的数字或符号，看看这样拆分后，是不是使计算变得简单多了。

①119+399=(　　)−1+400○1=(　　)

②207+88=(　　)+7+80○8=(　　)

③173+307=(　　)+(　　)+3+300+(　　)=(　　)

互动练习 1：

凯琳：3+5=8

山姆：5+4=9

乔伊：4+2=6

综上，山姆得票数最多，乔伊排第三。

互动练习 2：

① 1+6=7　2+5=7　3+4=7

② 1+7=8　2+6=8　3+5=8　4+4=8

③ 1+8=9　2+7=9　3+6=9　4+5=9

④ 10+60=70　20+50=70　30+40=70

⑤ 10+70=80　20+60=80　30+50=80　40+40=80

⑥ 10+80=90　20+70=90　30+60=90　40+50=90

互动练习 3：

7=10−3

18=20−2

5=10−5

7+18+5=10−3+20−2+10−5=(10+20+10)−(3+2+5)=30

所以，她们一共要花 30 元。

互动练习 4：

1+2+3+4+5+7+8=30 或

1+2+3+4+5+6+9=30

所以，该电视连续剧最多可以播 7 天。

互动练习 5：

7 种

1+2+9=12

1+3+8=12

1+4+7=12

2+3+7=12

1+5+6=12

2+4+6=12

3+4+5=12

互动练习 6：

32+76=108

58+49=107

20+30+51=101

80+20+35=135

互动练习 7：

①120，−，518

②200，+，295

③100，70，7，480

（习题设计：何　晨）

Mac & Cheese, Pleeeeze!

I like my teacher, Mr. Moore. I really do. But he comes up with the weirdest ideas.

"A lunch food election?" I roll my eyes. "Mayor Meatloaf ? President Pizza? "

My best friend, Luna, laughs. "Oh, come on, Caitlin. I think it sounds like fun."

"Class," Mr. Moore said this morning. "We are running the Spring Fest Lunch Election! "

"Huh? " we all asked.

Mr.Moore explained. "You'll each pick a lunch you'd like to eat at Spring Fest. Then you try to get other students to vote for your choice. The whole school will be voting—so good luck, and may the best lunch win! "

"It'll be a disaster," I tell Luna after school. "Remember last month's science project? "

Sure, we all liked the worm farm—until Sam and Joey got into a scuffle, knocked the worms over, and made a dirty, squirmy mess.

"That was gross," Luna admits. "But this is lunch. No dirt, no worms. At least, I hope not! "

Luna and I stop and take a look at Mr. Moore's election rules.

"What's the point? " I grumble. "Everyone will vote for Peppy Pizza."

"Not me," Luna says. "I'm voting for my favorite—Tofu Surprise."

Sometimes Luna is as weird as Mr. Moore.

I forget about the election until the next day on the bus.

"Check out my campaign posters for Tuna Melt," Annie says.

I raise an eyebrow. "You made posters? "

She unrolls one to show me her slogan.

Sam snorts. "You haven't got a chance. Wait till you hear my Broccoli Stuffed Potato speech."

I shake my head. "I can't believe you two even care who wins this goofy election."

"Don't you? " Annie asks.

"Yeah, right," I say. "Broccoli battles tuna. Big thrill! "

At school I check out the sign-up sheet. I guess I have to pick something.

Wait—nobody has signed up for Mac & Cheese? That's crazy! It's the best thing on the menu! I put down my name.

"Not bad," Annie says. "But, it's not as good as Tuna Melt."

At lunch I scarf down Mac & Cheese while Luna counts the votes she has lined up. "My brother and his chess club friends promised to vote for Tofu Surprise," she tells me.

"Really? That's their favorite lunch? "

Luna turns pink. "My brother said he'd bring in donuts if they voted for Tofu."

Joey looks up from his notebook.

"Counting your votes for Peppy Pizza? " I ask him.

"Nope. For all the lunches. See? Peppy Pizza is on top so far. Number 2 is..."

I stop to ask: "Broccoli Stuffed Potato? "

"Sam's been making lots of speeches,"says Joey.

"Where's Mac & Cheese? " I ask Joey.

He shows me. "Down at the bottom."

I can't believe it. Mac & Cheese is doing worse than Turkey Wieners!

This could be embarrassing. I'd better get some votes!

I find my sister, Sophie, on the swings. "What lunch are you voting for? " I ask.

"Peppy Pizza."

"But I need votes for Mac & Cheese."

Sophie smiles. "Okay."

"Okay, you'll vote for Mac & Cheese? "

"No. I still like Pizza."

Sophie's friend Rachel says, "I'll vote for Mac & Cheese if you'll push me."

Now I can count on two votes—Rachel's and mine. But if I have to get all my votes this way, my arms are going to fall off !

I spot my neighbor Charlie on the slide. "Will you vote for Mac & Cheese? " I ask.

"Sam wants me to vote for Broccoli Stuffed Potato."

I'm about to walk off. Then he says, "But you're my neighbor. And broccoli is gross."

Three votes. Well, it's a start. Still, I need more if I don't want to look like a total loser.

Who else can I get to vote for Mac & Cheese? I can't ask anyone in my class. They're all voting for their own lunches.

I could try Charlie's brother, Nick. He's my neighbor, too, even if he is only in kindergarten.

"Nick, do you like Mac & Cheese?"

"I just ate. I'm not hungry."

"What about when you are hungry?"

"But I'm not."

I finally talk all the little kids into voting for Mac & Cheese—except Nick. He says he's still not hungry.

Four more votes!

During math I try to think up a slogan.

Luna leans over. "I thought you didn't care about the lunch election?"

"I don't," I say, and cover up my notes. Me and my big mouth. Now I wish I hadn't teased the other kids for trying to get votes.

The next day some fifth grade girls see me putting up posters. "Cute!" one of them says.

"You've got my vote. I love Mac & Cheese!"

Her friends say, "Me, too."

Great! Three more votes. I'm up to ten. And I'm starting to like this election!

I wish I could add everything up on paper, like Luna. But if anyone saw me, they'd know how much I want the votes. I'd never live it down!

Sam is putting up posters, too.

I read them and laugh.

Then I see another poster.

Hmmph. That's not very funny.

Two kids from the soccer team are looking at my poster. I edge closer. "I like Peppy Pizza better," one of them is saying.

The girl says, "Yeah, but the Frisbee team is voting for Pizza. We can't do what they do."

"No way," the boy agrees. "The soccer team vote goes to Mac & Cheese."

Wow! That's twenty kids!

In class, Luna looks bummed. "They took Tofu Surprise off the menu. The cooks said it wasn't popular enough. Can you believe it?"

Actually, I can. But all I do is shrug.

"Now the chess club can't vote for it." Luna gives me a look. "Too bad you don't care who wins. We could all switch to Mac & Cheese."

I check to make sure no one else can hear me. "Maybe I do care—a little," I admit.

Luna smiles. "Well, in that case..."

There are 28 kids in the chess club, and Luna makes 29. Twenty-nine more votes!

Best friends are the best.

At choir practice, I whisper to the girl next to me. "Choir kids stick together. Vote for Mac & Cheese. Pass it on."

The news travels fast. Everyone nods and smiles. Yes! Thirteen more votes.

I run into Charlie on my way home.

"Guess what?" Charlie says. "I got my whole class to vote for Mac & Cheese tomorrow. All but Timmy. His sister Annie says he has to vote for Tuna Melt."

That's another 31 votes! Awesome!

At recess the next day, Joey comes over. "You're not at the bottom anymore!"

"Oh?" I try not to sound too interested. "So now I'm ahead of Turkey Wieners?"

"Even better," he says. "Peppy Pizza and Broccoli Stuffed Potato are tied for first, and Mac & Cheese is next!"

Wow! I'm just a vote behind Joey and Sam!

After class, Annie rushes up to me.

"Did you hear?" she says. "Sam and Joey got in a big fight over Sam's PIZZA IS FOR PIZZA FACES poster. Now Mr. Moore won't let either of them vote!"

One vote less for Peppy Pizza. One vote less for Broccoli Stuffed Potato. Woo-hoo! It's a three-way tie!

Now, if I can just get one more vote...

"Sophie, you're my sister," I say. "Can't you vote for Mac & Cheese?"

She plants her shovel in the sand. "PEPPY PIZZA."

So much for sisters.

Then Nick looks at me. "I'm hungry," he says. "I want Mac & Cheese."

That means...

"Say Cheese!" I yell. "Mac & Cheese, The Lunch You Love!"

I jump up and down. Luna gives me a high five.

Annie stares. "I thought you said it was a goofy election."

"Totally goofy," I say. "Totally weird. And I sure hope I win!"